Never Had a Friend

Live Show - Novel - Soundtrack - Picture Book

Written by Dr. Micah E. Johnson

www.DoctorMicahJohnson.com

I never had friends. We moved all the time.
New places, new schools, new city signs
I feared deep inside
that I may never find
best friends of my own
and I'll be left behind.

No friends to run,
to jump, to climb.
No friends to laugh
at my bad punch lines.
No friends to dine
or unwind in sunshine.
No friends to write
our own storylines.
But deep in my mind
I knew I would find
best friends of my own.
The very best kind.

While I wondered,
"Would I one day have a wonderful friend?"
I heard a rhythm in the kitchen,
and I listened in.
It was a teapot whistling in the wind.
The whistle made me wiggle, giggle, and grin.

I swayed, I swung, I spun, and then I tipped over the teapot and it burned my skin. I will never play in the kitchen ever again.

5

Burnt arm and all alone,
but still I felt strong!
Stronger than strong,
but when father came home,
something was wrong.

Our home, the homeliest home,
was only a loan and we no longer belonged.

We could not stay long.
We were to be gone
to a new place where I was unknown.
We packed our bags and moved along.

Goodbye to my bed. Goodbye to my sheets.
We slept on the sofa. We slept in love seats.
We sleep in the car, counting sheep in a jeep.
We slept on the floor.
We slept in the streets.

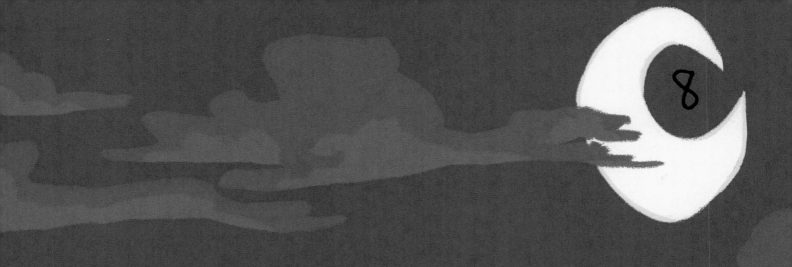

We slept on the park bleachers for weeks.

We slept in the freeze. We sleep in the heat.
My pillow was cold and hard as concrete.
All places we slept, it was so hard to sleep
until we found a shelter for families
with no place to sleep.

My new school was worse.
The kids laughed at my skin
and the tear in my shirt.
My feelings were hurt.

I felt like dirt.
The dirtiest dirt never felt worse.
I need help to feel better,
so I went to the nurse.

Ms. Nurse, they call me names
and my skin is to blame.
I am burnt and stained.

She said,
"Don't feel ashamed
because my skin is the same."

She explained
her grandmother's grandmother
trained her family to smile, even in pain.
I think I will do the same.

I was the new kid in school
and kids can be cruel
but I was saved by a jewel
who kept me safe from bullies and bulls.
The brightest of the bright
and the coolest of cool.

Deshaun was the coolest
in the pool of the coolest in school.

He said to me,   "Dude don't focus on fools.
You are kind, you are smart,
and you have the tools.
You'll be the friend who'll help me rule."

Our teacher was smart, the smartest of smart.
He taught us poetry, performance,
and also pie charts.
He taught us to use pain as a spark
to create, to imagine, to grow, and to restart.

The good and the bad, the light and the dark,
everything we see shapens our art.
The tragedies and triumphs, it all plays a part.

He said never fear if someday we depart.
Our friendship lives forever inside your heart.

Deshaun introduced me to Pencil Pete.
He was honest and sweet.
At lunchtime, he saved me a seat
and gave me
half his food
to eat.

But they called him bad and called him a thief.
They gave him more tricks than treats
but if he lived on a good street
they would call him a priest.
It made him sad.
He could not find peace.
They were afraid of his face.
They even called the police.

but when we were together,
we never felt grief.

Deshaun introduced me to Sarah Bubbles,
the only girl in our huddle.
She cuddled a duffel bag of puzzles
and shuffled through books without struggle.

Her father had a bundle of money
that was quadruple double
our richest uncles'.
But she was humble
and played with us
in the puddles.
She was our muscle
and stood up to teachers
to save Pete from trouble.

We were the phenomenal four
best buddies in a bubble.

My new life was lovely
with my three best buddies.
We followed each other,
like four little duckies. We rehearsed our play.
We helped each other study.
We walked home together,
like four little puppies.

Even in heat, when our shoes were sunny.
Even in rain, when our shoes were muddy.
Even in snow, when our shoes were slushies.
Even if dusty, yucky, and mucky,
if we were together,
we always felt Lucky.

My friends made me glow glorious glows.
I never had a friend like those.
But, one day, I felt low, the lowest of lows.

With holes in my clothes and open shoe soles,
I live in the place where the homeless goes.
Deshaun and Pete will not want to be bros.
I will lose my best friends
I will fall on my nose.

One day I decided, it is time alas,
to tell my friends the scariest secret I ever had.
I showed them the homeless shelter
where I lived with dad.

I said, "I live right here, and it makes me sad.
I have holes in my shirt but that is all I have.
Sorry I did not tell you, please don't be mad."

Deshaun said, "I am so sorry
that you live in a place like this,
but I will never disrespect you or our friendship."
Friends never tease, and
friends never quit.
Friends will be friends
if you are poor or rich.
Friends don't dismiss.
Friends come for defense.

I wish you had a home, I wish you lived in bliss
But we're in a gritty city
where kids get kicked, not kissed.
Just use your gifts
to tell our story
and maybe it will all make sense."

Later that day, in the nighttime
my three friends all combined
and secretly designed a plan to be my lifeline.

They ripped holes in their clothes
to look just like mine.
Deshaun, Pete, Sarah, and me, all aligned,
with holes in
our clothes,
a friendship goldmine.

That day was the very first time
I wore my tore clothes and I felt just fine.

Aha! Epiphany! I had a breakthrough.
The best friend I ever had, coming to my rescue.
And now, I knew how to be a best friend too.

Best friends are genuine, honest and true.
Best friends are consistent,
dependable, and loyal like glue.
Best friends are by your side
with tissue when you feel blue.
Best friends make sure you
do the right things too.

Best friends are strong,
helping you to push through
the icy muddy slush
that seeps through
holes in your shoes.

Best friends are trustworthy
and keep pinky promises too
Best friends do not change
if your clothes are old or brand new
Best friends don't make excuses,
that's not what they do.
Best friends always pursue
and value your point of view

The four of us in chorus were glorious.
The story of us
From phobias to euphoria.

Enjoying the joy in us. We were victorious.
Exploring with warriors of joyfulness
Rejoicing, for no one enjoyed more joy than us.

Better than besties.
The Friendliest Friendlies
The very best friends
and the very best Frenzies

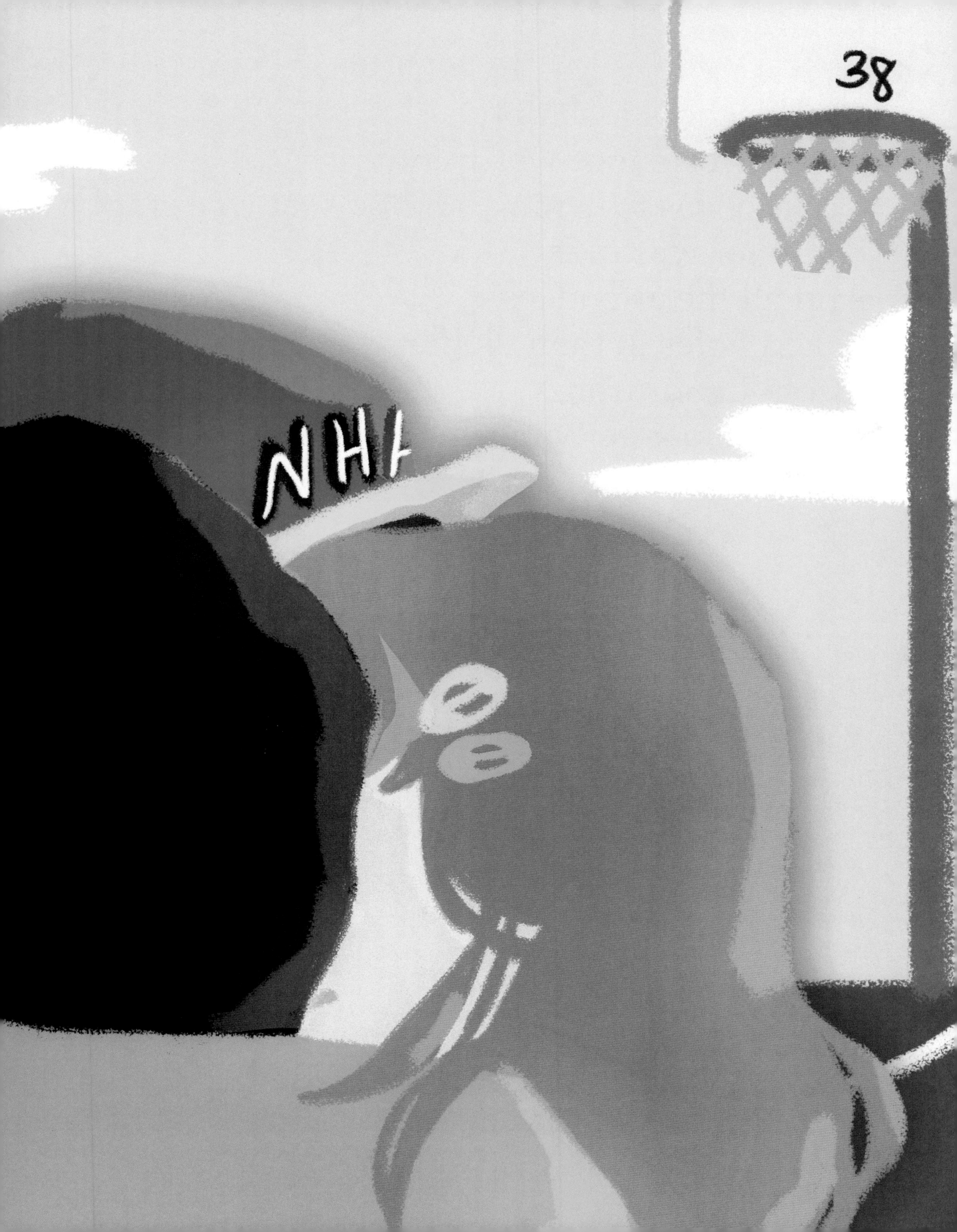
NH

At the school assembly
Our performance was trendy
No face was frowning, and no seat was empty
Laughter was plenty
And all the attendees
Poked holes in their clothes
to join in our frenzy
We were perfectly in sync.
Perfect. Plain and simply.

the strong and the brittle,
the pears and the pickles, were totally tickled
and gathered in giggles.

We laughed all day
and every day after,
the weather forecaster
predicted more laugher
No matter what happened
the laughter came faster.

We sung through sorrow
and danced through disaster,
The world was our stage
and we were the ringmasters.

No tough time could test me
No sadness could stress me
because my best friends would bless me
Bester than the best
The very best of besties.

47

Friends who befriend,
Friends who defend,
Friends pinned together
in a blend
of colors, sizes, and origins.

Friends who attend
Friends who comprehend
Friends to depend on in losses and wins
Through thick or thin. Friends to the end.

49

Grateful. Faithful. Unbreakable.
Gainful. Stable. Unshakeable.
Graceful. Able. Unmistakeable.
Gayful. Playful. Unescapable.

My life had immensely improved
I still had torn shirts and torn shoes
But now I cruised through
the homeless shelter in a groove
With a smile, awesome cool mood,
and nothing to prove.
My father was waiting, he was not amused.
He said, I have bad news, we have to move.
Confused. Without a clue,
I disapproved.
I used every tool I could use.

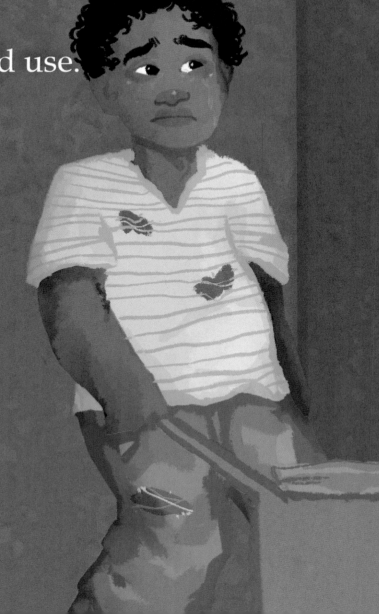

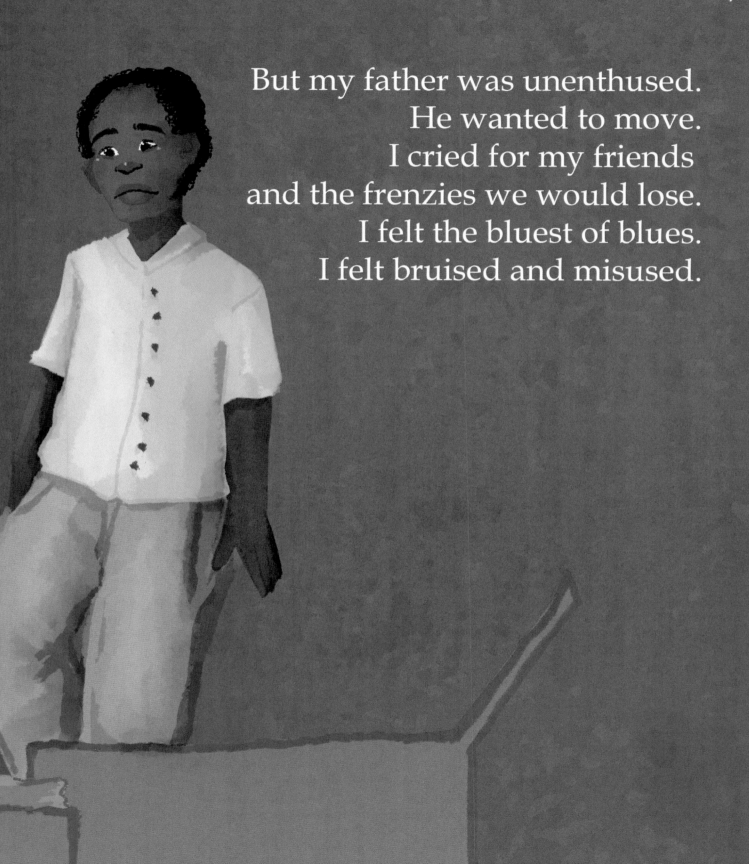

But my father was unenthused.
He wanted to move.
I cried for my friends
and the frenzies we would lose.
I felt the bluest of blues.
I felt bruised and misused.

My heart broke
I choked on every word that he spoke
We were moving in an hour
and I did not have a vote
We were leaving behind all we could not tote
No time to say goodbye.
No time to leave a note.
Hope floated away with a hold in its boat
My cheeks were soaked.
There were spider webs in my throat.
My stomach was loaded with
sour artichokes and egg yolks
My lungs were in the snow
without a coat

All I heard was crows coos
and lonely frog croaks
The whole world was laughing,
and I was the joke

We were moving again
The Frenzy must end
My tummy tumbled in a tailspin
The wind at my window
sounded like weeping violins

But suddenly, my grimace turned into a grin
when I heard the voice of Mr. Miranda from
deep within say to me again,
"A friendship never ends".
You will live in my heart forever.
Together. My friends.

Never Had a Friend

Live Show - Novel - Soundtrack - Picture Book

Written by Dr. Micah E. Johnson
www.DoctorMicahJohnson.com

Please Bless Us with Five Stars on Amazon!

Meet the Author

I am Dr. Micah E. Johnson. I am a researcher, speaker, teacher and feeder of future leaders. I am a blend of Mother Goose, Dr. Seuss and The Roots. I study why bad things happen to kids, the places live, the things that they did, and the ways they forgive. I speak and teach to anyone in my reach on children's health, community unity and sustainable peace. I dream of safety for children everywhere, but some kids have no home and no healthcare. It is so unfair but I know that you care and are willing to share what you have to help us get there. Let's clean up this world! I will start by shampooing my hair. My dream is to clean up the bad, the sad, and the trash. I would give everything I have to help heal the wounds of the past. Fast as the flash, I would do it in a dash. However, these dreams cost a ton of cash. I hate to ask, but please support us on social media and send us a few dollars from your stash. DoctorMicahJohnson@gmail.com or www.DoctorMicahJohnson.com

Made in the USA
Monee, IL
09 January 2021